First published by Parragon in 2007 / This edition published by Parragon in 2007
Parragon
Queen Street House
4 Queen Street
Bath BA1 1HE, UK

ISBN 978-1-4054-7266-1

Printed in China

FUN
THINGS TO
MAKE
AND DO

Written by Kath Smith
and Charlotte Stowell

Illustrated by Gary Walton

PaRragon

Bath · New York · Singapore · Hong Kong · Cologne · Delhi · Melbourne

Photography by Peter Canning

Crafts made by Charlotte Stowell, Katy Rhodes and Sue Hunter-Jones

Design by Chris Scollen and Sarah Williams

Contents

Getting Started

This book is full of creative craft projects for adults and children to work on together, using everyday items and materials which are easy to buy. The things you need are listed at the top of each project.

Takes less than an hour

12
3
9
6

Look out for the helpful little clock symbol. It will tell you roughly how long each project will take. Some crafts are quick to finish. Some need to dry overnight.

Getting ready

Find everything you need for a project, and set it up before you start. Cover the table and floor with newspaper, old sheets or plastic rubbish bags. Make sure children wear an apron or old T-shirt to protect clothing. But remember that getting a little messy is part of the creative fun!

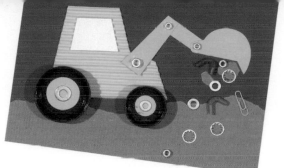

How to get the most fun out of projects!

- As far as possible, let children pick projects for themselves. They are more likely to be enthusiastic. A good way to choose is to show them the Look-it-up Gallery on p90.

- You may need to do some parts of the project steps, such as cutting out basic shapes ready to decorate. But try not to take over. Children will have more fun and a greater sense of achievement if they do most of the work themselves.

- If a project has a long drying time, tell children before they start, so they don't expect to finish it in one go.

- Young children find it hard to concentrate for a long time. You may need to let them finish off some things later.

- The ideas in the book are suggestions only. Encourage children to think of ways to adapt them, using different colours, materials and subjects.

Art Materials

Glue

The best glue to use for these projects is either non-toxic PVA or rubber-solution glue. Both are available from craft shops.

• Pour the glue into a plastic tub or jar with a wide base, so it won't tip over.

• Use an old paintbrush or plastic spatula to apply glue.

• Paste glue onto the background, and not onto the item you are sticking down. That way fingers get much less sticky!

Paint and Brushes

Use either acrylic paints or good-quality poster paints. A cheap set of different sized brushes is ideal.

• Pour paint into plastic pots or use plastic paint trays.

• Put water for brush washing in big jars that won't tip over.

• Always wash brushes in water, and wipe with kitchen roll between colours.

• Acrylic paint needs to be washed off clothes immediately, so make sure children are covered up.

Printing

Most young children tend to dip printing blocks into paint and then onto paper without thinking about position. Try to get them to start their picture in the middle of the paper so they don't run out of space or go too near the edge.

Busy Box

Keep a 'busy box' of useful things, such as cardboard tubes, shoe boxes, crisp tubes with lids, round cartons, washing powder tablet boxes, coloured sweet foils and bubble wrap. You never know when they might come in handy for crafts!

Scissors

Safety scissors can be used to cut paper and card. Felt, fabric and string will need to be cut with sharper scissors. If it is not appropriate for your child to use sharp scissors, you will need to do the cutting yourself.

Splat Monsters!

1

Use a brush to blob three different colours next to each other in the middle of the paper. Use plenty of paint.

2

Blow the paint blobs around with the straw to mix them and to make a spidery pattern on the paper.

3

When dry, add eyes with thumb prints. Then use a cotton bud dipped in black paint to make the pupils.

4

Draw arms and legs with a crayon or felt-tip pen. You could make your monster wave or dance!

This splat
monster has
been made
using a
straw.

Takes less
than
an hour

12
3
9
6

To get a different
effect, use your
finger instead of a
straw to spread
out the paint.

13

Caterpillar Prints

You will need:
coloured paper · pencil
bright or metallic paints
cork · paintbrushes
wobbly eyes (optional)
scissors

Choose a sheet of brightly coloured paper. Lightly draw a wavy pencil line across it as a body guide.

Dip a cork into some paint. Press it down onto the paper at the start of the wavy line. Continue printing along the line.

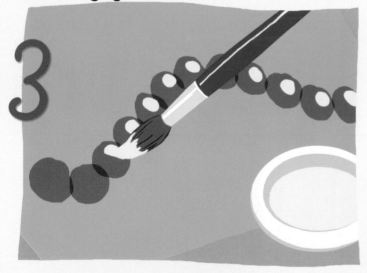

Use a paintbrush or fingertip to blob dots along the caterpillar in a different colour.

Now paint in the caterpillar's legs all along the body, using a thin paintbrush.

To finish your picture, stick or paint on two wobbly eyes. Then cut out or tear a large leaf shape from green paper. Stick it underneath the caterpillar.

Takes less than an hour

12
3
9
6

If you don't have a cork, dip your thumb in paint and use it to print the body.

You don't have to use wobbly eyes. You can paint the eyes instead.

Fuzzy Sheep

You will need:
small pieces of sponge
thick paper for the background
thick paint · felt · glue
scissors · sequins
cotton bud

Dip a piece of sponge in some white paint and print a cloud shape for the sheep's body.

Cut out the face and leg shapes from felt (an adult may need to help with this).

Allow the paint to dry. Then glue the face and legs onto the body.

Glue on sequins for the eyes. It is easier to put the glue on the face than on the sequins.

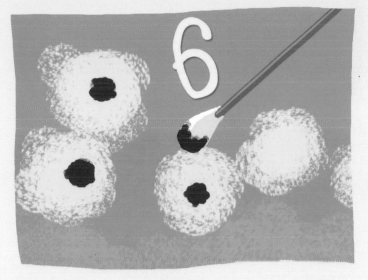

Use different pieces of sponge dipped in paint, to print the grass and flowers.

When the paint is dry, use a cotton bud to paint the centre of the flowers.

Takes less than an hour

Try making this fuzzy rabbit, too. His nose and ears are made from felt scraps.

Before you start painting, dab your sponge on some newspaper a few times, so the paint is not too runny.

Ice-cream Dream

You will need:
coloured paper • paints • brush
kitchen towel • scissors
brown parcel paper
strip of thick card
cotton bud

Choose three colours for your ice-cream blobs. Mix a little white paint with each colour to make pastel ice-cream shades.

Dip one edge of the card strip in brown paint. Print a criss-cross pattern and a fan shape on the brown paper.

Cut out a cone and a wafer shape. Glue the cone onto the background. Leave room to paint the ice-cream blobs above.

Dip a piece of scrunched-up kitchen towel into each ice-cream paint, and print blobs above the cone.

18

When dry, cut out a chocolate-flake shape from a piece of brown painted card, and glue in position, as shown.

Glue on the wafer and add red thumb-print cherries. Add spots of white with a cotton bud to make the cherries shiny.

Takes more than an hour

Try adding glitter or dots of different colours, to create 'hundreds and thousands'!

Practise dabbing blobs on scrap paper before you paint your ice cream.

19

Glue Painting

You will need:
pencil · thick paper
rubber-solution glue
paints · brushes · masking tape
glitter (optional) · pen

1 Draw a simple ghost shape onto thick paper. The simpler the outline, the better.

2 Tape down the paper to a work surface, using the masking tape.

3 Paint your design with rubber-solution glue, using an old paintbrush. Leave to dry.

4 Use a thick paintbrush to paint two or three different colours onto the background.

5

When the paint is completely dry, rub off the glue with your finger to magically reveal the picture.

Use a pen to draw a face on your ghost.

Takes more than an hour

Try painting glue swirls on your picture, and sprinkling on glitter for a sparkly effect.

21

Bubble Dinosaur

You will need:
coloured paper for the dinosaur
(green and yellow)
red paper for the background
pencil · paints · bubble wrap
sponge · scissors · sequin
black felt-tip pen

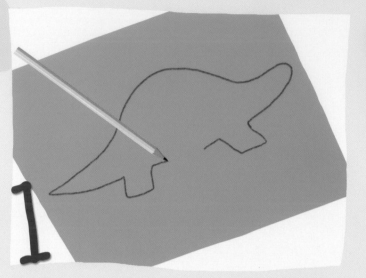

Draw a simple dinosaur shape onto the green background paper.

Sponge thick yellow paint onto a sheet of bubble wrap, with the bubbles facing up.

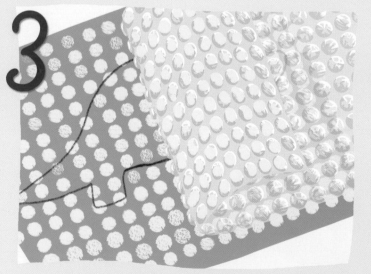

Carefully place the painted bubbles over the dinosaur outline. Press down, lift off the bubble wrap and leave to dry.

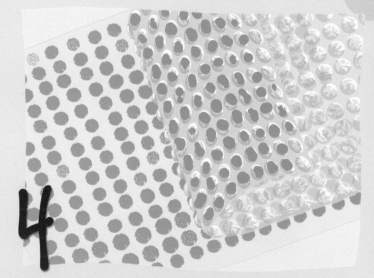

Using the same method, print a strip of green bubbles on the sheet of yellow paper, and leave to dry.

Cut out the dinosaur shape. Then cut the strip of yellow paper into triangles. Glue the dinosaur onto the red paper.

Stick the triangles down the dinosaur's back. Glue on a sequin for its eye, and draw in a mouth.

Takes less than an hour

You could use this method to create other creatures, too. A crocodile would work well.

You could cut out your dinosaur and hang it up.

Cake Wrapper

You will need:
long strip of coloured paper
sellotape · things to print with
(eg: sponge, corks, cotton buds,
modelling clay) · things to stick
on (eg, sequins and stars)
glue · scissors · paints

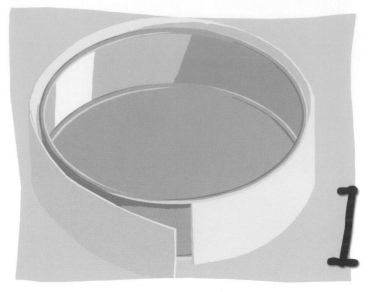

Cut a strip of coloured paper to fit round your cake, with a few centimetres overlapping at the end.

Make a simple butterfly-shaped printing block out of modelling clay. Alternatively, you could use thick card.

Sponge thick paint onto your printing block. Print a line of shapes along the strip of paper. Wash the block between colours.

When the paint is dry, print the butterflies' bodies, as shown, using a long, thin oval-shaped modelling clay block.

24

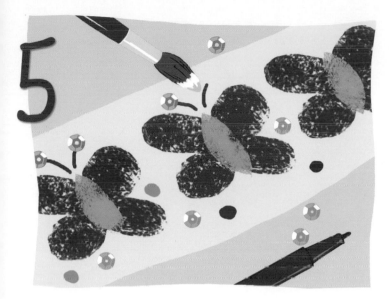

5

When dry, decorate the strip using sequins, gems, felt-tips or anything else you think would look pretty.

6

Finally, wrap the strip around the cake and secure with tape. For a hidden join, you could use double-sided tape.

Takes less than an hour

12
3
9
6

Print any design you like. Just change the shape of your printing block.

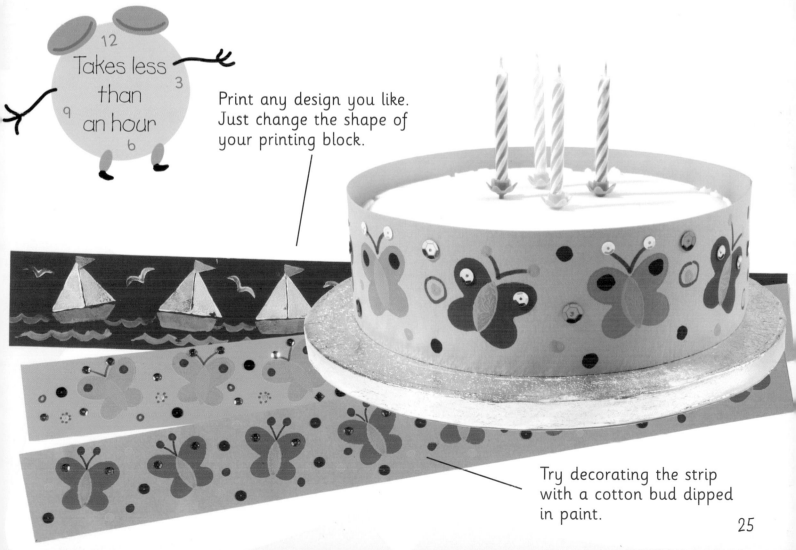

Try decorating the strip with a cotton bud dipped in paint.

Let's Get Digging!

You will need:

coloured paper for background
corrugated card
brown paper · plastic lids · glue
useful bits and pieces (eg, washers,
nuts and bolts, beads etc.)
scissors · paintbrush

1

2

Draw a simple digger shape onto the corrugated card and cut it out (an adult may need to help with this).

Tear a long strip of brown paper. Stick it along the bottom of the background, as shown, to make the earth.

Arrange the digger shapes on the page. When you are happy, glue them onto the background.

Paint the lids with thick paint. When dry, stick them onto the digger for the wheels. You can add card hub caps if you like.

Glue on some bits and pieces to make the rubble. Try bits of drinking straw, scraps of screwed paper or washers, nuts and bolts.

You can buy ready-coloured corrugated card. If you don't have any, just paint ordinary corrugated card instead.

Takes more than an hour
12 3 9 6

Experiment by adding extra bits and bobs to customize your vehicle.
Try other vehicle shapes, too.

Nuts, bolts and paper clips look effective, but are not suitable for children under 3 years.

27

Funky Foam Cat

You will need:
coloured sheets of craft foam
scissors • card • pen • glue
sheet of coloured card for the
background • a pair of wobbly
eyes (optional) • pencil

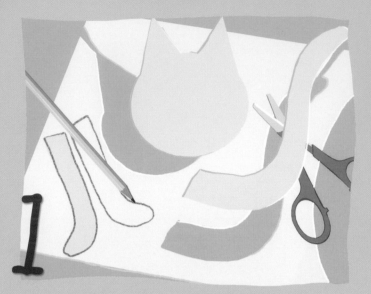

1 Draw simple shapes onto card for a cat's head, tail, body and legs. Cut them out (an adult may need to do this).

2 Carefully draw around all the cut-out shapes on a sheet of coloured craft foam.

3 Cut out the shapes. Metal scissors will make a cleaner cut, so an adult may need to do this step.

4 Cut out some stripes from a different coloured foam. Glue the stripes onto the body and head of the cat.

5 Arrange the body, head, legs and tail on the background. Then glue them into position.

6 Cut out a nose and whiskers from spare bits of foam, and glue in place. Glue on the eyes.

If you don't have wobbly eyes, glue on some foam scraps or draw eyes with a felt-tip pen.

Takes more than an hour

To make a funky foam tiger, use orange, black and white foam.

Eggshell Mosaic

You will need:
several eggshells (depending on the size of the finished picture)
paints · sponge or brush
card · glue · paintbrush

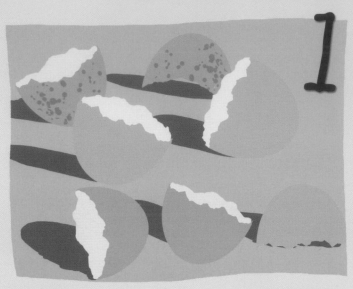

1

Wash and dry your eggshells using kitchen towel. The more eggshells you have, the better.

2

Paint the shells with different coloured thick paint. They may need a few coats. Allow them to dry overnight.

3

Paint the card green and allow it to dry. Then draw a simple flower shape on the card.

4

Break up the shells into small pieces. Keep different colours in different boxes ready to make your picture.

5

Brush thick glue onto your design. Stick down the eggshell pieces and leave to dry before touching.

If you paint the eggshells white first, then paint colour over the top, your mosaic will look much brighter.

You can create any design you want using this idea. Use as many colours as you like.

12

Needs to dry overnight

3

9

6

Papier-mâché Snail

You will need:
Kitchen towel • PVA glue
pipe-cleaner • wobbly eye
empty ice-cream tub
coloured cardboard (such as the
side of a box, painted)
paints • brush

1

Pour PVA glue into a large plastic tub. Tear off two sheets of kitchen towel and dip them in the glue until covered.

2

Twist the kitchen towel round, until it is like a rope. It is best to do this over the glue tub, to catch drips!

3

Curl the rope round into a spiral shape to make the snail's shell. Leave the spiral to dry on a flat, wipe-clean surface.

4

Repeat the process to make a second rope. Curl it into the snail's long, thin body. Leave it to dry overnight with the shell.

5

When dry, paint the snail's shell and body with brightly coloured thick paint. Leave to dry.

6

Glue the body and shell onto the card background. To finish, add a bent pipe-cleaner and a wobbly eye.

Needs to dry overnight

Decorate the shell with stripes or dots.

If you don't have a wobbly eye or pipe-cleaner, draw or paint the features instead.

Glitter Stones

You will need:
flat pebbles · pencil · glue
glitter · stick-on gems
sequins · paint · paintbrush

1

Paint a pebble with thick paint. Allow to dry. Draw a simple fish shape onto the pebble.

2

Fill in the fish shape with glue. Glue on a sequin or a stick-on gem for the eye.

3

Sprinkle glitter all over the fish, and shake any excess onto a sheet of paper.

4

Use a paintbrush to add bright green seaweed around your glittery fish.

If you don't have gems or sequins, paint the eyes instead.

Takes less than an hour

12

3

9

6

Experiment with different designs. Try decorating your pebbles with more sequins and stick-on gems to create an extra-special effect.

These glittery pebbles make great gifts. You can use them as paper weights, or simply as decorations.

Collage Robot

You will need:
glossy magazines
aluminium foil or foil sweet
wrappers · glue · card
pencil · scissors
coloured paper

Tear magazine pictures into pieces. Keep different colours in separate piles, so they don't get mixed up.

Draw a simple robot head, body, legs and arms on card. Cut the shapes out (an adult may need to help).

Cover the robot shapes with glue. Then stick on the coloured magazine bits. Allow the shapes to dry.

Trim around the outside of each robot shape, to neaten the edges. An adult may need to help with this stage.

5

Arrange the robot shapes on the page and glue into place. Add balls of screwed—up foil for the eyes, and a semicircle of foil for the mouth.

If you like, glue a card control panel onto your robot's tummy, with screwed—up foil control buttons.

This black background really makes the shiny bits stand out.

12
Takes
more than
an hour
9   3
6

37

Make a Jigsaw

You will need:
felt tips or crayons (if creating your own picture) or a picture from a magazine • A4 card scissors • pencil • ruler

1 Draw a picture on a piece of A4 card. Keep the shapes simple enough to make a child's jigsaw.

2 Colour in the picture. If you are short of time, stick a magazine picture onto A4 card instead of drawing something.

3 Divide up the picture into ten sections — you can either use wavy lines, or draw straight lines with a ruler.

4 Cut along the lines carefully, so you have ten jigsaw pieces (an adult may need to help with this).

Make your jigsaw picture from anything you like. This one was made out of collage.

Keep your jigsaw pieces safe inside an envelope.

12

3

9

6

Takes less than an hour

This jigsaw has ten pieces. To make more difficult jigsaws, cut up your picture into even more pieces.

Flying Saucer

You will need:
two small card dishes • silver paint
a plastic cup cut in half
three bendy straws • pencil • glue
felt-tips • scissors • tape • beads
buttons • coloured sweet foil
card for alien or alien toy

1

Use a pencil to make three holes in the bottom of one of the dishes.

2

Paint both dishes silver and allow to dry. Alternatively, use foil pie plates.

3

Trim 8cm off the long end of each straw. Push the straws through the holes, with the short part inside. Tape in place.

4

Glue a card alien or toy alien to the top of the other dish. Glue the rim of the plastic cup and stick on top.

5

Glue the two dishes together. To finish, stick on decorations such as pieces of straw, beads, buttons or little foil balls.

Coloured metallic paints create a shiny effect.

If you prefer, simply paint decorations on your flying saucer.

Takes more than an hour

Swimming Turtle

You will need
paper plate · paper bowl
green and red tissue paper
card · pencil · glue
big glue brush · scissors · tape
beads for the eyes

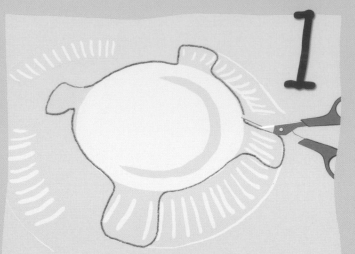

1

2

Draw the legs onto a large paper plate and cut out, as shown.

Cut out a head and tail from card. Tape into position on the leg-shaped plate.

3

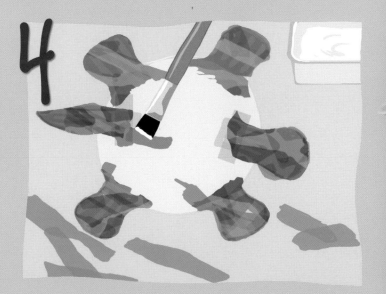

4

Paint the outside of the paper bowl with glue. Stick strips of green tissue paper all over, to cover it. Leave to dry.

Now cover the legs, head and tail with tissue paper strips. When dry, trim the tissue paper around the edges.

5.

Spread glue onto the underside of the bowl and stick it on top of the plate. Glue on red tissue-paper spots. Leave to dry. Then spread white glue over the top for a shiny finish.

You could decorate your turtle's shell with shiny foil dots.

PVA glue dries to a hard, shiny finish.

Stick on beads for eyes or create eyes by screwing up paper into tiny balls.

Needs to dry overnight

12 3 6 9

Volcano Pen Tub

You will need:
strip of card 30 x 10cm
ruler • pencil • tape
cardboard circle • kitchen towel
PVA glue thinned with water
paint • big brush • glitter

1

Draw a line 3cm from the edge of the card strip. Snip along the line (an adult may need to help here).

2

Curl the strip into a circle, with the ends overlapping. Tape the ends together and tape to the base, as shown.

3

Tape balls of screwed up kitchen towel around the base of the tube, to make more of a volcano shape.

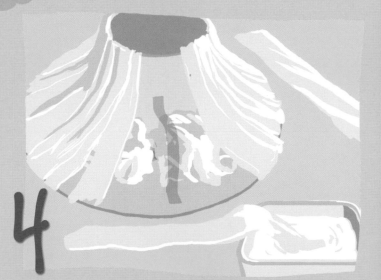

4

Dip kitchen towel strips into the thinned PVA glue. Layer them over the tube and base. Leave to dry overnight.

When completely dry, paint the volcano base in thick green paint. Leave to dry (the airing cupboard is a good place).

Add red and orange paint around the top. Then drizzle it down the sides with a big brush, and sprinkle with glitter.

You can store all your pens and crayons in the volcano.

To make the red paint really pour down the side of your volcano, try dribbling it with a big spoon instead of a paint brush.

12
3
9
6
Needs to dry overnight

Shiny Fish

You will need:
card · self-hardening clay
rolling pin · plastic knife
small bowl of water · paintbrush
ruler · plastic straw
metallic paint · glitter
ribbon (optional)
pencil · scissors

1 Draw a simple fish shape, about 10cm long, and cut it out.

2 Roll out the clay till it is about 1cm thick. Cut around the fish with a plastic knife.

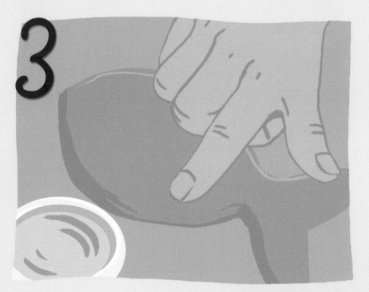

3 Dip your fingers in a bowl of water and smooth the edges of the fish.

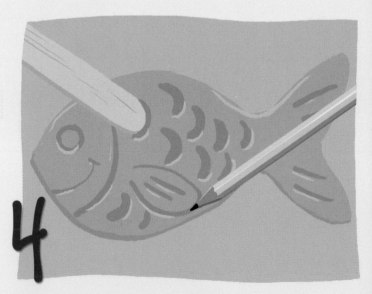

4 Use a pencil, straw or brush to make scale and fin patterns on both sides. Draw a face.

46

Make several
fish, and hang
them together,
to create a
shoal.

Use metallic
paint to give
extra sparkle!

If you use
ordinary
paint, varnish
when dry to
add shine!

Needs
to dry
overnight

12
3
9
6

5

Push a pencil through the clay,
to make a hole in the top.
Leave to dry overnight.

6

Paint the fish and sprinkle with
glitter. When dry, thread a
ribbon through the hole.

Box Truck

You will need:
cardboard boxes painted white
tape · glue · paint · paintbrush or
sponge · round lids · scissors
coloured card · aluminium foil (or
foil card) · shiny bottle tops

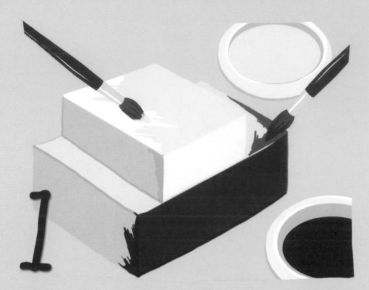

1 Tape down the box flaps. Glue a small box on top of a bigger box, as shown. Paint brightly using a brush or sponge.

2 Paint four lids for the wheels. When dry, paint hub caps on the inside, or stick on some card circles.

3 When dry, glue the wheels onto the sides of the lower box. Leave to dry.

4 Add some other details, such as foil windows and a front grill, as shown.

5

Finally, glue headlights to the front. You could use shiny bottle tops or foil circles.

Takes more than an hour
12
3
6
9

If you paint your boxes white first, the colours will be much brighter!

Save left-over cardboard boxes and lids for this type of project. Then, when you feel like making something, you'll have a few different sizes to choose from.

A silver shiny grill and windows look effective.

49

Pirate Ship

You will need:

shoe box • two cardboard boxes
(one smaller than the other)
long cardboard tube • tape
coloured paper • scissors • straws
black felt tip • plastic lid • 8 corks
paints • paintbrush • glue

1 Paint the shoe box and the middle-sized box blue. Paint the smallest box red, and the tube dark blue. Leave to dry.

2 Draw a pirate flag on the sheet of paper with a felt-tip pen. You can do any design you choose.

3 Glue the two smaller boxes inside the shoe box, one on top of the other, as shown in the picture.

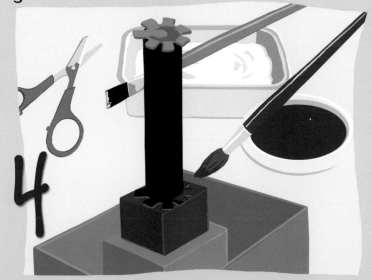

4 Snip around both ends of the tube, as shown. Glue it on top of the red box. Cover the join with red paint.

Fold over the top and bottom edges of the flag. Dab with glue and stick to the tube. Glue the plastic lid on top.

Stick three red paper squares along each side of the ship. Paint six corks black, and two red. Stick them to the ship, as shown.

Takes more than an hour

You could add extra features to your pirate ship, such as a gang plank.

Paint the boxes white first, if you want the red and blue colours to look really strong and bright.

Plastic play figures make the ideal crew for your pirate ship.

Try to use a sturdy shoe box for the boat. It will last much longer.

Techno Paper

You will need:
sheets of plain wrapping paper
or brown parcel paper
plastic wheels and blocks
sponge · paints
cork · pencil

1 Unroll a sheet of plain wrapping paper on a flat surface. Hold down the ends with something heavy.

2 Choose a long, thin building block for printing. Carefully sponge blue paint along one side of it.

3 Print blue lorry cabs all over the sheet, not too close together. Print red lorry sides with a second block, as shown.

4 Use the end of a cork to print the black wheels, and the end of a pencil dipped in white paint for the hub caps.

Cogs, wheels and other construction toy bits make great printing blocks. Experiment with shapes and colours.

Takes less than an hour

This pattern was made by rolling toy wheels in different coloured paints, and then pushing them across the paper.

Metallic or shiny sheets of plain wrapping paper make extra-special gift wrap!

Flower Paper

You will need:
sheets of plain wrapping paper or brown parcel paper • interesting items to print with (such as pen lids, corks, cotton buds and buttons) sponge • paints

Place a sheet of wrapping paper on a flat surface. Use a sponge dipped in paint to print flowers all over it.

When dry, dip a finger in a different colour and print the centres of the flowers. Be careful not to smudge them.

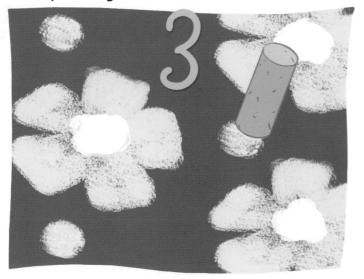

Use the end of a cork to print circles between the flowers. Remember – you can choose any colours you like.

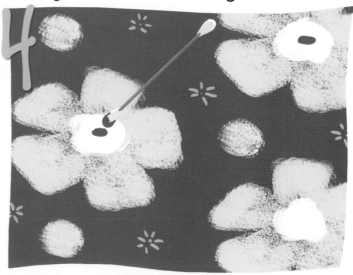

Use a cotton bud dipped in a different colour to print small circles in the very centre of each flower.

Before you paint on the wrapping paper, try out your printing shapes on a spare piece of paper.

Takes less than an hour

12
3
9
6

The tiny flowers on this sheet were made using the end of a pen lid.

The hearts on this wrapping paper were created using two thumb prints.

55

3D Cards

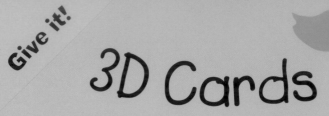

You will need:
self-hardening modelling clay
rolling pin · plastic knife
coloured card · paper
tissue paper · glue · brush
paint or felt tips · sequins

1 Use a rolling pin to roll out a slab of self-hardening yellow modelling clay to a thickness of about 1cm.

2 Cut out a duck shape with a plastic knife. It may help for an adult to draw a card template first, to trace around.

3 Fold a sheet of coloured card in half. Stick a rectangle of coloured paper on the front. Glue on strips of blue tissue.

4 Glue on the duck once it is hard. Paint or draw a beak and eye onto it. Glue on sequins to add extra sparkle.

Needs to dry overnight

12
3
9
6

If possible, leave your clay shapes to dry overnight — you will get a better result.

Simple shapes and designs work the best. This clay star has been covered with silver glitter.

Number Cards

You will need:
coloured craft foam · card
pencil · scissors · tissue paper
foil or sweet wrappers
stick-on gems
glue · paintbrush

Draw a large number on a flat sheet of foam, and carefully cut it out. An adult will need to help with this.

Tear up strips of coloured tissue paper and paste them onto the foam number.

Carefully trim the ragged edges to neaten up the look of the foam number.

Stick the number onto a folded sheet of card, and decorate with bits of foam.

Takes less than an hour

12
3
6
9

This idea can be used to make birthday cards for anyone — from age 1 to 100!

Multicoloured craft foam makes a simple but effective design.

Use stick-on gems, sequins, screwed-up balls of foil or foil strips to decorate your card.

Ladybird Box

You will need:

cheese triangle box · plastic lid
black card · white crayon
sponge · green and red paint
glue · beads
stick-on gems (optional)

Draw around the plastic lid on the black card. Add six legs, a head and antennae.

Cut out the body and legs carefully. An adult may need to help with this.

Sponge-paint both halves of the cheese box, inside and out. Sponge the plastic lid with thick red paint.

When dry, stick the card body on the box top. Then stick onto the red lid. Decorate with beads for the spots and eyes.

If you want to protect your box, coat it with a thin layer of spray varnish (done by an adult).

Use smaller lids if you want more than one bug on your box.

Takes more than an hour

Create your own crazy bugs using bright colours and shiny gems.

61

Photo Frame

You will need:
multi-coloured lolly sticks
(or painted plain ones)
thick card · glue · paint · brush
thread for hanging · tape

1

Cut four strips of thick card. They must be slightly shorter than the lolly sticks.

2

Glue three coloured lolly sticks to each strip of card. Leave to dry.

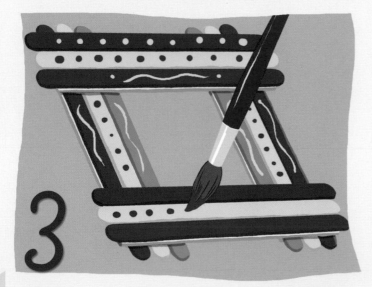

3

Make the lolly card strips into a frame and glue together. Decorate with spots and stripes.

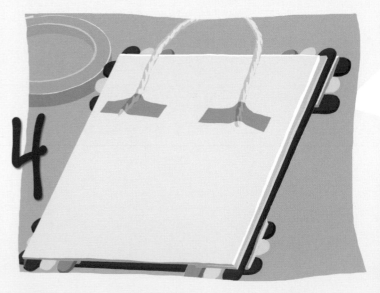

4

Glue a piece of card to the back of the frame, leaving the top edge open. Tape thread on the back, to hang it up.

Slip a favourite picture or photograph into your frame through the open slot in the top edge.

You could also decorate your frame with stickers or stick-on gems.

If you don't have coloured lolly sticks, paint ordinary ones in bright colours. They may need a couple of coats of paint.

Treasure Box

You will need:
small shoe box with lid
gold paint · sponge
paintbrush · small card shapes
buttons · glue · string
felt (optional)

1

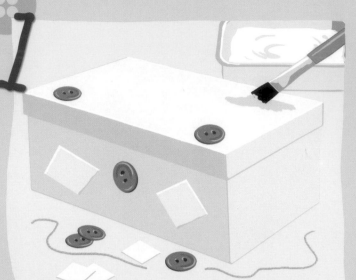

Put the lid on the box. Glue buttons, string and card shapes over the box and lid.

2

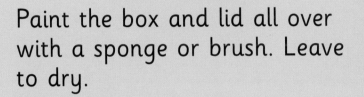

Paint the box and lid all over with a sponge or brush. Leave to dry.

3

Sponge gold paint over the top of the buttons, string and card shapes.

4

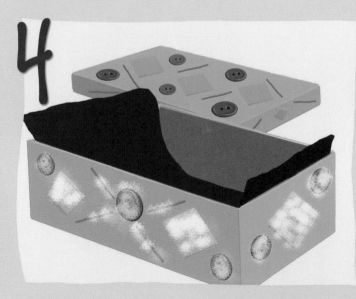

When the paint is completely dry, stick some felt inside the box to make a lining.

Remember to leave the lid on while you stick on the buttons, string and card shapes. This will ensure the lid always fits properly.

The treasure box can be used to store anything precious, such as jewels, model pieces or top secret things!

Stick-on gems could be added when the box is finished, to create an extra-special finish.

Bouncing Spiders

You will need:
coloured plastic pan scourer
five furry pipe-cleaners
pair of wobbly eyes (optional)
glitter • glue pen (or glue and
glitter) • string for hanging
glue • brush

Twist four of the pipe-cleaners together in the middle, to make the spider's legs.

Push a small length of pipe-cleane through the middle of the scourer, as shown.

Twist the small piece of pipe-cleaner round the legs, as shown in the picture. Spread out the legs and bend to shape.

Stick the two wobbly eyes on with glue. Use the glitter glue pen to make a pattern on the spider's back.

66

Takes less than an hour

12
3
9
6

If you want to hang up your spider, push a length of string through the scourer and tie a knot.

If you don't have a glitter glue pen, don't worry. Your spider will still look fantastic!

You don't need to use wobbly eyes. Draw your own eyes, cut them out and glue them on.

67

Straw Danglers

You will need:
sheet of acetate (or plastic)
multi-coloured drinking straws
glue • brush • scissors • wool or
thin ribbon • beads • pen

Carefully spread a thin layer of PVA glue all over the sheet of acetate or plastic.

When the glue is tacky, stick the drinking straws down onto the acetate. Dry overnight.

Draw a diamond shape on the straws (the straws must be vertical). Cut out the shape. An adult may need to help.

Thread a length of wool through the middle straw. Thread a bead onto the end. Tie a knot underneath to secure it.

Use thin ribbon instead of wool for a pretty look.

Make different straw shapes and thread them onto a long length of wool or ribbon, with beads between each one.

Needs to dry overnight

12
3
9
6

You don't have to buy new beads. You could use dried pasta or old beads from broken necklaces.

Shiny Foil Balls

You will need:
aluminium foil · ruler · sponge
thick paint · gold thread
large blunt needle
scissors

1 Cut or tear three strips of foil. Screw one strip into a ball, as tightly as you can.

2 Use a ruler to hit the ball, to compact it and smooth out the crinkles.

3 Make two more balls. Sponge thick multi-coloured paint over all the balls and leave to dry.

4 Push a needle threaded with gold thread through the balls. Tie a knot after each ball.

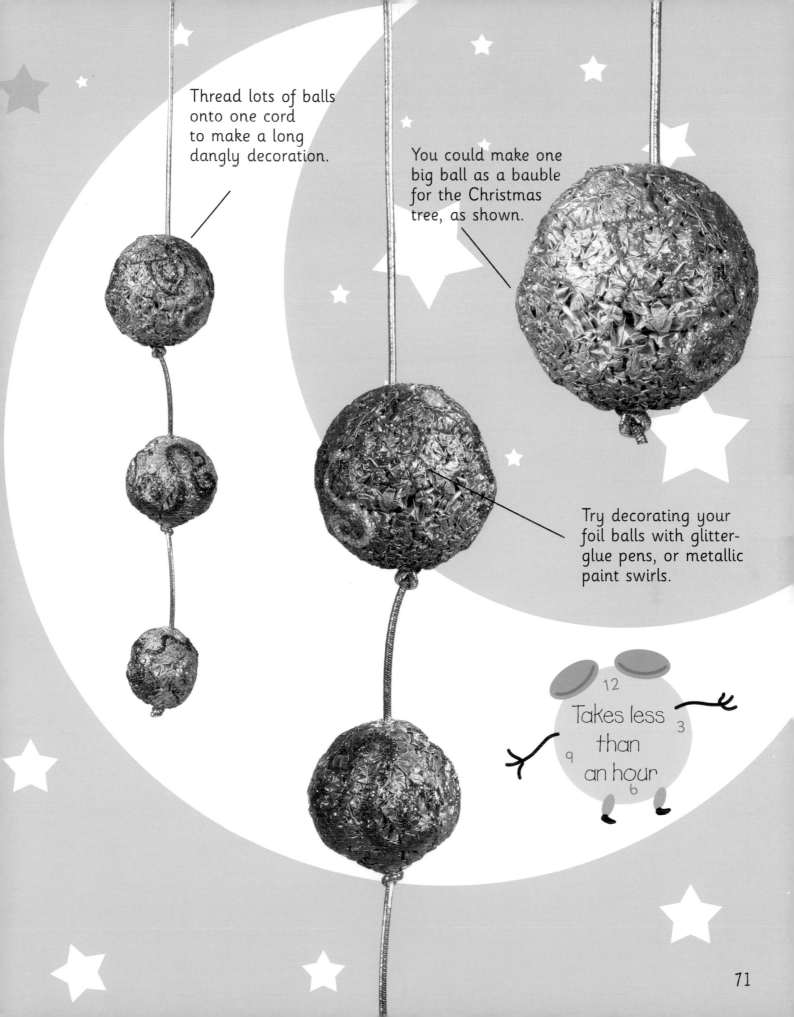

Thread lots of balls onto one cord to make a long dangly decoration.

You could make one big ball as a bauble for the Christmas tree, as shown.

Try decorating your foil balls with glitter-glue pens, or metallic paint swirls.

Takes less than an hour

Felt Creatures

You will need:
two matching felt circles
coloured felt scraps · scissors
tape · cotton wool · glue · brush
thread for hanging · wobbly eyes
or beads · 2 feathers

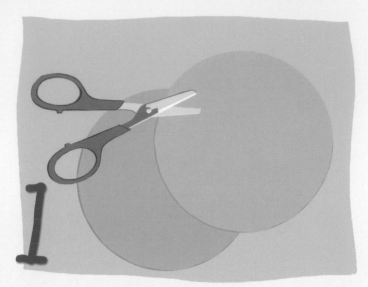

Carefully cut out two matching felt circles using sharp scissors. An adult may need to help with this.

Cut legs and a crest from felt scraps. Tape on the back of one circle. Then tape on the feathers and a thread loop.

Place a ball of cotton wool in the middle, as shown. Apply glue around the edge of the second felt circle.

Glue the second circle over the top of the cotton wool, as shown. Press down the edges and leave to dry.

72

Cut out a felt triangle for a beak. Glue the bead eyes and beak on the front, to finish your creature.

Try using this idea to make other felt creatures, such as this dotty octopus.

If you don't have any beads, cut out eyes from felt or paper instead.

Takes less than an hour

73

Window Lights

You will need:
clear plastic yogurt pot lid
different coloured tissue paper
glue · brush · ribbon · sequins
or stick-on gems

1

Cut a simple Christmas tree shape from tissue paper. Tear up different coloured tissue paper into small pieces.

2

Paint the plastic lid with glue. Cover it with torn-up tissue paper. Then stick the Christmas tree on top.

3

When the tissue paper is dry, decorate the lid with sequins or stick-on gems to give it extra sparkle.

4

Brush glue around the edge and tie a ribbon round it, making a loop at the top (an adult will need to do this).

You could punch a hole in your decoration, and thread ribbon through it, to hang it up.

Use a glitter pen, or glue and glitter, to add a sparkly rim around the edge of your window light.

Hang up your finished decoration in a window. When light shines through, the colours really glow!

75

Christmas Stocking

You will need:
sheet of coloured A4 card
glue · brush · scissors · pencil
lots of bits and pieces for
decoration (eg, tissue paper, craft
foam, foil, glitter, ribbon, gems
and sequins) · tape

1

Fold the A4 card in half. Draw a stocking shape to fill the card with one edge along the fold. Cut it out.

2

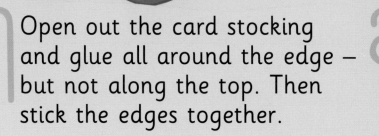

Open out the card stocking and glue all around the edge – but not along the top. Then stick the edges together.

3

Decorate the stocking using paint, pens, glitter, tissue and sparkly bits.

4

Tape a loop of ribbon to the back of the stocking, so that you can hang it up.

If you are going to give your stocking as a gift, you could make a matching gift tag to go with it.

This idea is great for using up scraps of foam, paper, stick-on gems and sequins.

When you have decorated your stocking, neaten up the edges by trimming them.

Takes less than an hour

12

3

9

6

77

Angel Decoration

You will need:
paper plate · sheet of white felt
square of pink felt (10 x 10cm)
felt scraps for hands · scissors
lengths of white wool (20 x 16cm)
foil · glue · brush · paper clips
felt-tip pens · cotton wool
elastic band

1

Glue the white felt to half of the paper plate. Cut the plate in two. Trim round the edges to neaten.

2

Cut out two felt hands, and a strip 12cm x 5cm for the arms. Glue on the hands. Fold over the strip and stick down.

3

Roll the covered half-plate into a cone, and glue. Use paper clips to hold it while the glue dries. Stick on the arms.

4

Wrap cotton wool in the felt square. Secure with an elastic band. Draw the face. Tie the wool in the middle, and stick on as hair.

5

Glue the head into the top of the cone. Then brush the other half of the paper plate with glue and cover with foil. Cut it in half to make two wings, and glue them onto the angel's back. It helps to secure them with paper clips while they dry.

Make a halo for your angel by twisting a length of foil tightly and curling it into a circle.

You can also make the head by painting a polystyrene ball with pink paint and gluing it onto the body.

12
Takes more than an hour
3
9
6

Decorate your angel with beads, stick-on gems and sequins to catch the light.

79

Monster Mask

You will need:
sheets of coloured craft foam
sheet of A4 paper • pencil
glue • elastic cord • scissors

Fold the A4 paper in half. Draw the mask outline onto the paper, as shown. Cut out.

Trace around the mask outline on a sheet of green craft foam, and cut it out.

Cut two small eye holes in the mask, about 6cm apart. An adult will need to help.

Cut out shapes of coloured foam. Glue them onto the back, around the edge.

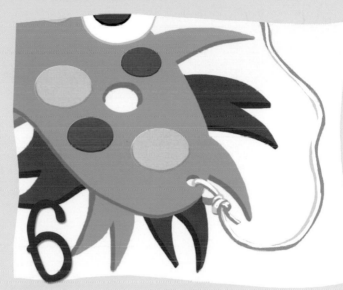

5 Cut white and black foam circles for the eyes and stick them to the front of the mask. Add coloured dots.

6 Make a small hole on each side and thread elastic through. Secure with knots.

Move the position of the black eye pupils to make your monster look in a different place.

Try adding foil dots for a different look.

12
Takes less
than
an hour
3
9
6

You can use this method to make all kinds of animal masks, from tigers to rabbits.

Make a Crown

You will need:
gold or silver card
gold or silver card shapes
glue · scissors · pencil
stick-on gems · paper clip
tape measure

1

Cut out a strip of gold card. Measure the child's head, but about 60cm should fit most heads.

2

Cut out some large card circles and diamonds. Glue them along the top edge of the head strip.

3

Cut out smaller card circles and diamonds. Glue them onto the gold strip. Decorate with stick-on gems.

4

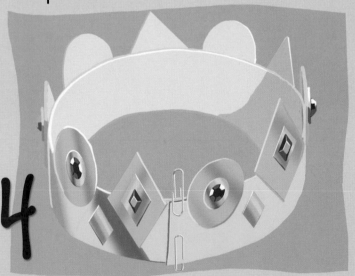

Wrap the crown around the child's head. When it fits, secure it with a paper clip, before gluing.

82

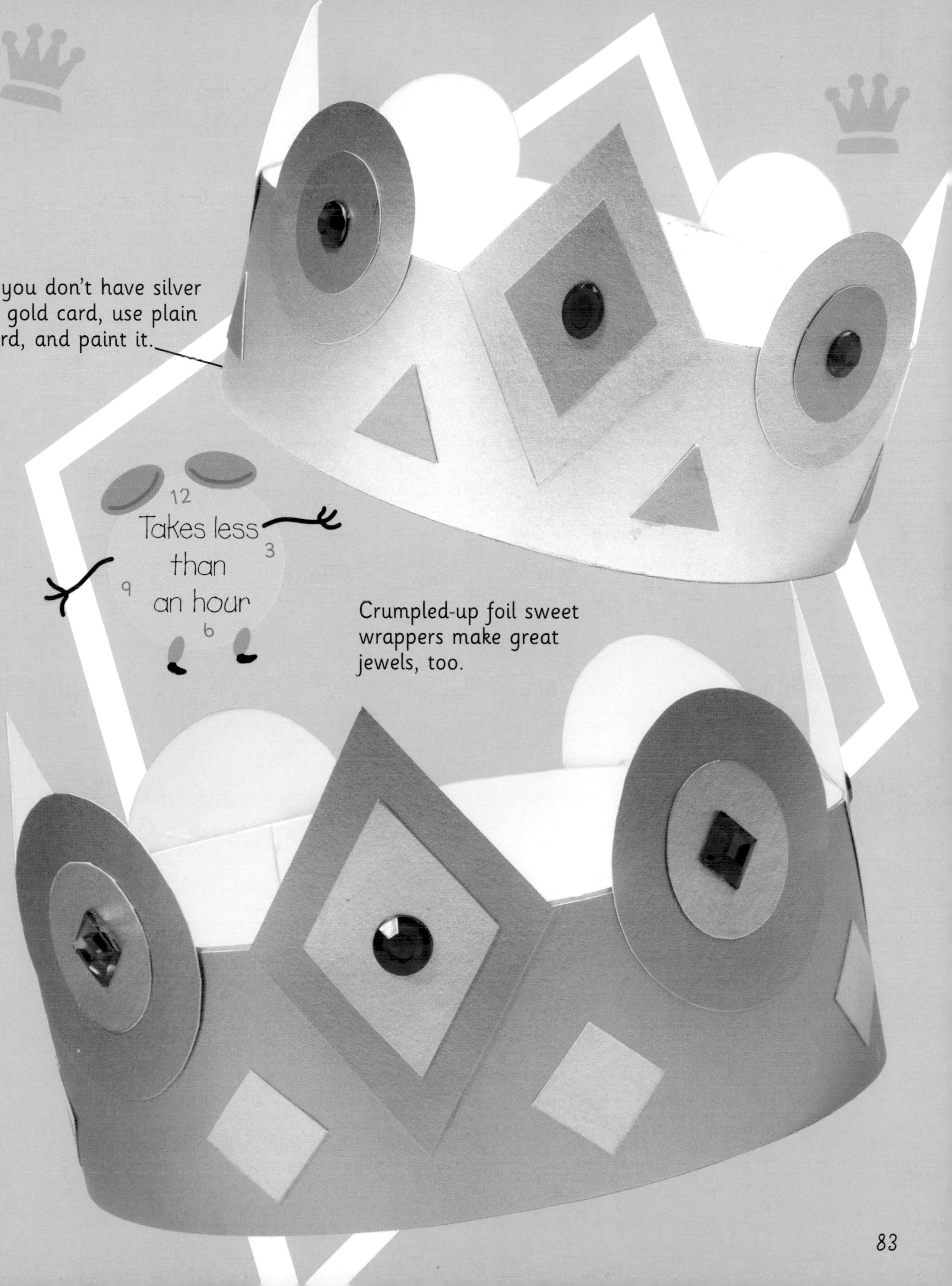

If you don't have silver
or gold card, use plain
card, and paint it.

Takes less
than
an hour

12
3
6
9

Crumpled-up foil sweet
wrappers make great
jewels, too.

Skittles

You will need:
6 clean empty drinking-yogurt
bottles with lids • paint • brush
glue • coloured card
6 white paper circles
felt-tip pens • paper scraps
ribbon • sequins

1 Paint the yogurt bottles in bright colours. When dry, glue on the lids.

2 Decorate each bottle. You could glue on strips of paper, ribbon and sequins.

3 Stick down the paper circles on the coloured card, as shown in the picture. Write numbers 1 to 6 in the circles.

4 When dry, set up the skittles on the card – ready to be knocked down.

Takes more than an hour

12
9
3
6

Roll a small ball to knock down your skittles. Then add up the score.

You can make all your skittles match, or decorate each one differently — it's up to you.

Fishing Game

You will need:
paper plate · blue paint
sheets of craft foam
paintbrush · paper-clips
string or thread · scissors
lolly sticks · felt-tip pen

1

Paint both sides of the paper plate blue. Leave the plate to dry.

2

Draw a starfish shape on yellow craft foam and cut out. Draw or stick on foam eyes.

3

Unbend a paper clip to make a hook. Tie to one end of the string. Tie the other end of the string to the lolly stick.

4

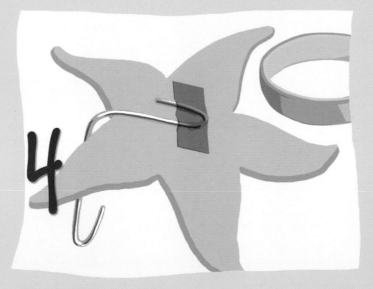

Tape an unbent paper clip to the back of the starfish. Then turn the starfish over and bend up the hook, as shown.

To play this game,
make lots of different
foam sea creatures – such as
fish, crabs and seahorses.

Use your fishing
rod to hook up
the sea creatures
from the plate.

12
3
Takes less
than
9
an hour
6

Decorate your
sea creatures
with stripes or
spots cut from
scraps of craft
foam.

87

Pin the Tail

You will need:
card cut from a big grocery box
pencil · scissors · paint
big brush · felt · coloured foil
pin or sticky putty · thread

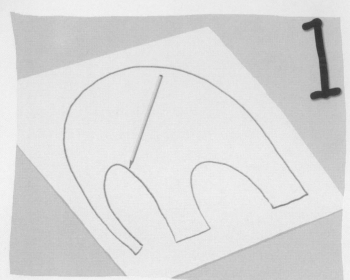

1

Draw out a simple elephant shape onto the thick card. Cut it out.

2

Paint the elephant. You can use the semi-circle section from under the legs for the ear.

3

When dry, glue felt and foil decorations onto the elephant. Glue down the ear. Mark a spot where the tail should go.

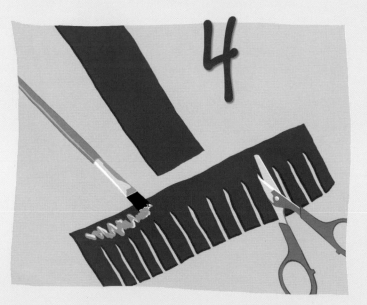

4

Cut a long felt tail. Make a tassel for the end, as shown. Tie the tassel on tightly with some thread.

5

Use either a pin or a big blob of sticky putty to stick the tail onto the elephant.

Tape some ribbon or gold thread to the back of your elephant, to hang it up.

Put on a blindfold and try to guess where the tail should go by feeling your way around the elephant.

Takes more than an hour

12
3
9
6

Jacob

Emily

Daniel

Sarah

Jack

Anna

If you prefer, decorate the elephant by painting on stripes and dots.

Smoothed-out foil sweet wrappers make good decoration.

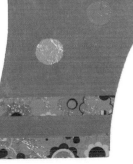

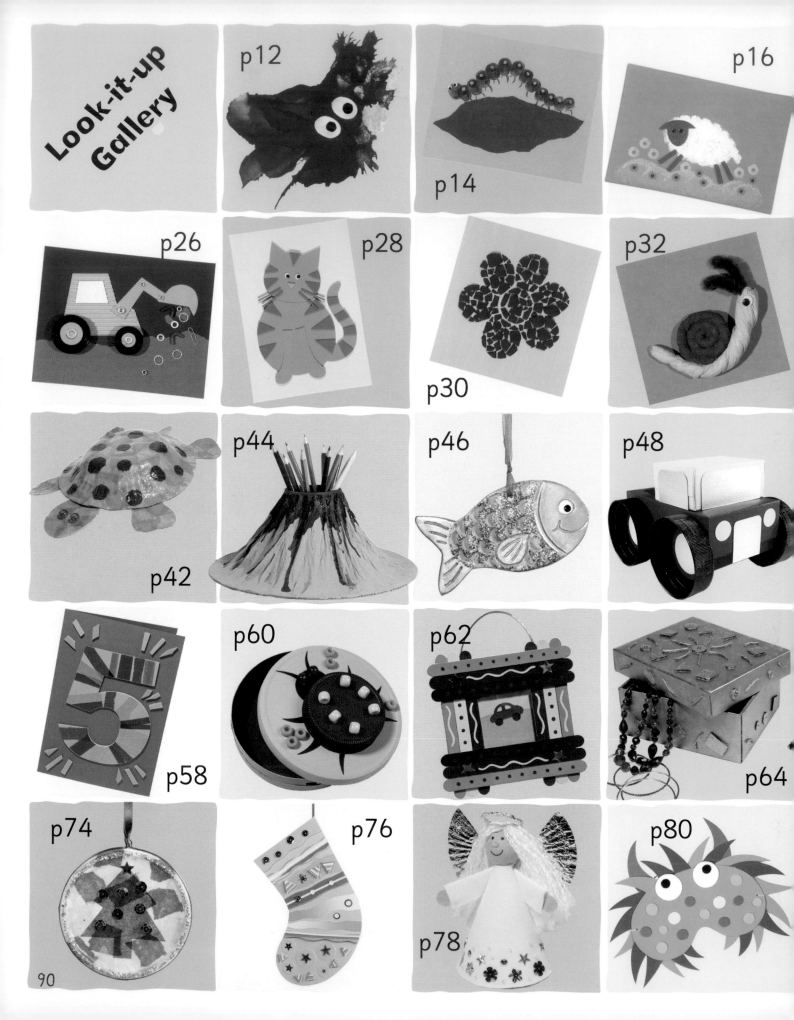

Look-it-up Gallery

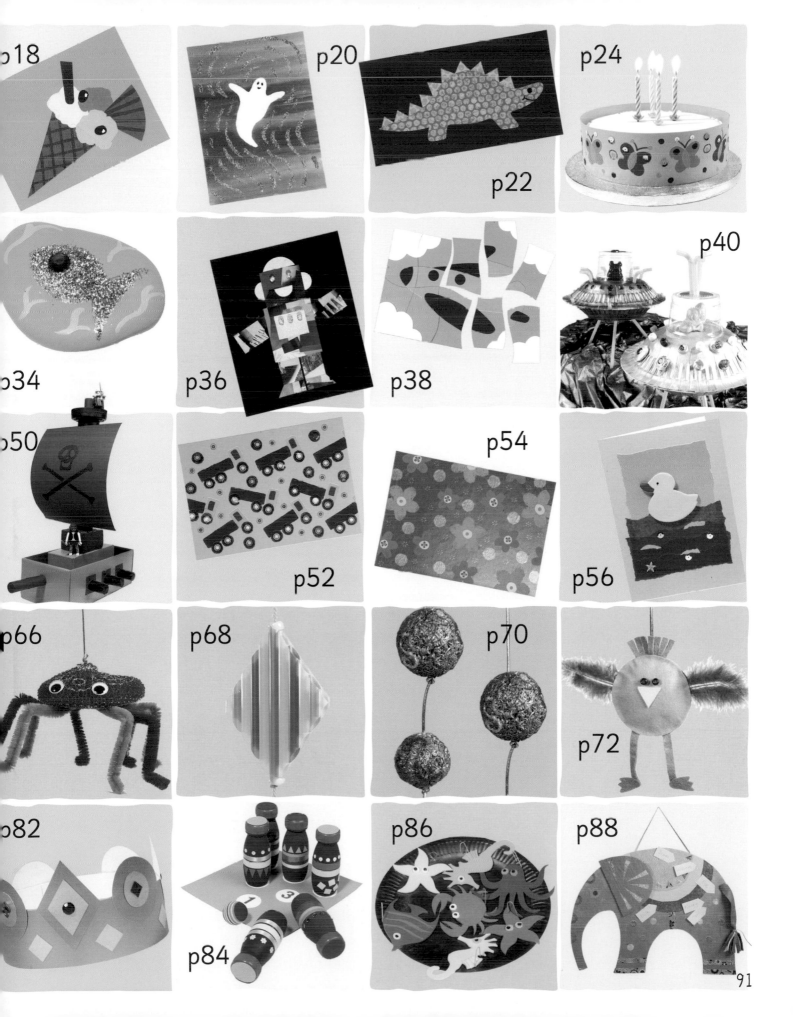

p20

p22

p24

p34

p36

p38

p40

p50

p52

p54

p56

p66

p68

p70

p72

p82

p84

p86

p88

91

Index